JAY McINERNEY

The Queen and I

A
BLOOMSBURY
QUID

First published in Great Britain 1996

Copyright © 1996 by Jay McInerney

The moral right of the author has been asserted

Bloomsbury Publishing Plc,
2 Soho Square, London W1V 6HB

A CIP catalogue record for this book
is available from the British Library

ISBN 0 7475 2895 0

Typeset by Hewer Text Composition Services, Edinburgh
Printed by St Edmundsbury Press, Suffolk
Jacket design by Jeff Fisher

As the tired light drains into the Western suburbs beyond the river, the rotting pier at the end of Gansevoort Street begins to shudder and groan with life. From inside a tin-roofed warehouse, human beings stagger out into the steamy dusk like bats leaving their cave. Inside the shed one can make out in the dimness a sprawling white mountain, the slopes of which are patched with sleeping bags, mattresses, blankets, cardboard and rafts of

3

plywood. An implausible rumour circulates among the inhabitants of this place that the white mesa is made of salt which was once, when there were still funds for municipal services, spread on the icy city streets in winter; at present the rusting warehouse serves as a huge dormitory and rat ranch. At dusk the inmates rise to work, crawling out into the last light to dress and make-up. Down on the edge of the high-way along the foot of the pier, the shiny cars of pimps and johns wait alongside the beat-up vans from the rescue missions and religious orga-nisations, ready to compete for the bodies and souls of the pierdwellers.

Covering the waterfront, I watch

as three queens share a mirror and a lipstick, blinking in the slanted light outside the shed which houses the mountain of salt. One of them steps away a few feet, creating a symbolic privacy in which to pull up his skirt demurely and take a torrential leak. A second lights up a cigarette and tugs on a pair of fishnet hose. The third is my friend Marilyn, queen of Little West 12th Street. It's my first night on the job.

I ran into Marilyn in the emergency room at Saint Vincent's a couple of days before. I went in for gingivitis, my gums bleeding and disappearing up the sides of my teeth from bad nutrition and bad drugs. It's a common street affliction, another credential in my downward slide toward authenticity. Marilyn had a broken nose, three cracked ribs and assorted bruises from a trick who had second thoughts.

'I thought you had a pimp, Marilyn,' I said, watching a gunshot victim bleed on a gurney.

'The pimp, he get killed by the Colombians,' said Marilyn. 'He never protect me anyways, the bastard. He punch me hisself.' Marilyn laughed through his nose, then winced with pain. When he could speak again he said, 'Last time my nose is broken it's my papa do the breaking. He beat the shit out me when he find me dressed in Mama's wedding gown. I'm holding the lipstick and he opens the door of my room. Smack me good, scream at me, call me a dirty little maricon, he don't want no maricon for a son. The boy last night, he was like that, this big bulging muscle New Chursey boy. After I do him, he start hitting, calling me faggot. A lot them like that, they don't like what they want. Hey, man,' he said, scrutinising me with new interest. 'Why don't you be my pimp? I give you five dollar on every trick.'

It was a measure of my prospects that I thought it was a pretty good offer. In fact, I'd been similarly unemployed by a recent murder and was sleeping in Abingdon

Square Park. I was dealing halves and quarters of coke out of a bar on 13th when my man got whacked and I was left without a connection. Before that I'd been in a band but the drummer ODed and the bassist moved to LA.

When I first met Marilyn I was living in a cellar in the meat district. Marilyn worked all night, and I was awake jonesing on coke or crack and trying to write. I am a songwriter, you see, a poet Mo-dee. There is beautiful, ugly music inside me, which plays in the performance space deep in my mind. Walking the streets, doing the bars, I hear snatches of it in the distance, above the subliminal bass line of the

urban heartbeat. I am most attuned
to it in moments of transport, when
I'm loaded on cheap wine or crack.
Sometimes I'm dead certain that one
more drink, one more hit and I will
grasp its essence and carry it back
with me to the other side. A student
of lowlife, zoologist of artifice and
aesthetician of ugliness, I am living
here in the gutter like Prince Hal,
biding my time, waiting to burst
forth like a goddamned sun.

A refugee from the western suburbs, I used to skip school and take
the bus into the city. I hung out on
St Mark's Place and the Bowery,
copping the look and the attitude
of punk, discovering Bukowski and
the Beats in the book shops. Re-

turning to the subdivisions of Jersey was an embarrassment. The soil was too thin for art. No poetry could ever grow in the grapefruit rinds of the compost heap. Ashamed of my origins, neither high nor low, I dreamed of smoky bars and cafés, steaming slums. I wanted to get down and dirty. I believed that the lowest road would lead me to the height of consciousness, that to conceive beauty it was necessary to sleep with ugliness. I've been in that bed for several years now. So far nobody's knocked up.

Like Dylan says – Someday everything is gonna be different, when I paint my masterpiece. I will be rich and famous and photographed with models who will suddenly find me incredibly attractive – my goodness, where have I been all their short naughty long-legged lives? – and I will do a lot of expensive designer drugs and behave very badly and ruin my promising career and end up right back here in the gutter. And I'll wish I'd been good to the people I met on the way up because they'll piss all over me when I meet them again on the way down. And I'll write a song cycle about it. It'll be excellently poignant, even tragic.

Marilyn grew up in Spanish Harlem, where he was christened with the name Jesus, a delicate boy with a sweet face who is plausibly a piece of ass as a girl. He wants to get married and live the kind of life I grew up in. Except he wants to do it as a woman. At night he looks longingly out over the Hudson at the dim glow of suburban New Jersey the way I used to look over from the other side at the lights of Manhattan. He wants a three-bedroom house in the burbs which he can clean and polish while he waits for a husband who works in the city. There's a huge Maxwell House sign across the river from the Gansevoort pier, and he told me once that when he wakes up as the average American workday is ending he remembers the tuneful Maxwell House ads he saw when he was a kid, dreaming about being the perky wife percolating a pot of coffee for sleepy hubby.

The doctor who gives Marilyn his hormone shots says that more than half of the – what shall we call them? – people who get the operation get married, and that more than half of those who do don't tell their husbands about their former lives as men. I personally find this just a teensy bit hard to believe. But Marilyn believes and he's saving up to pay for the operation.

Poor Marilyn with his broken snout. In his business he needs to be able to breathe through his nose. I decide to give it a shot. Could be a song in it. Plus I'm stone broke.

So as the sun goes down beyond

the river into the middle of America where the cows are coming home to their barns and guys with lunchboxes and briefcases are dragging ass home to their wives I am trudging toward the meat district with Marilyn, who is wearing fishnet hose under a green vinyl miniskirt and a loose black top. The Queen and I.

'How I look, honey?' Marilyn asks.

'Looking bad, looking good,' I say.

'This my Madonna look. Those Jersey boys – they love it.'

By now I'm sure you've guessed that Marilyn is currently a blonde.

The smell gets worse as we

approach Washington and Gansevoort, which is Marilyn's beat – the warehouses full of dead meat, the prevailing smell of rot inextricably linked in my mind with the stench of urine and excrement and spent semen. A sign says 'VEAL SPECIALISTS: HOT HOUSE BABY LAMBS, SUCKLING PIGS & KID GOATS'. Whoa! Sounds like that shit should be illegal, you know what I'm saying?

With darkness falling on the meat-packing district a slow and funky metamorphosis is taking place. Refrigerated trucks haul away from loading docks while rough men in bloody aprons yank down metal shutters and padlock sliding doors. The suffocating smell of rotting meat hangs over the neighbourhood, and, when the breeze blows east of the Hudson, infiltrates the smug apartments and cafés of Greenwich Village – which is the only good thing I can say about this stench.

As the trucks disappear toward New Jersey and upstate, strange creatures materialise on the broken sidewalks as if spontaneously generated from the rotting flesh. Poised on high heels, undulant with the exaggerated shimmy of courtship – a race of lanky stylised bipeds commands the street corners. They thrust lips and hips at passing cars, those cars that pass this time of night, the area not exactly being on the direct route to anything except Hell or Hoboken. Passenger wheels that find their way here cruise slowly down the unlit cobbled streets, circling and returning to pass the sidewalk sirens. Sometimes a car slows to a stop near one of the posing figures who leans over the driver's window to consult, haggle and flirt, sometimes to walk around the car and slip inside the passenger door, disappearing to reappear a few minutes later.

The sirens of Washington Street come in all sizes, colours and nose shapes and in this light not all of them are hard to look at. One lifts a halter top to expose a lunar pair of taut white breasts as a red Toyota with Connecticut plates crawls past. It's just barely conceivable that some of these sports in the cars who transact for five minutes of sex believe that they're getting it straight. But ladies, I wouldn't count on it. I mean if it's your fiancé gets busted down here you might think about cancelling the band and the tent and the cake. Or maybe not. They're probably good family men, most of them. And so long as clothes and make-up stay in place no one needs to start parsing his proclivities and worrying about whether he's straight. Sometimes the cops

sweep through to meet arrest quo-
tas; johns who find their pleasure
interrupted by a sudden official rap
on the car window almost always
act shocked when the cops expose
the gender of their sexual partners
with a playful tug of the waistband
or the not-so-playful rending of a
skirt.

The clientele is nothing if not
diverse, arriving in limos and Che-
vies, Jags and Toyotas. Whenever a
certain homophobic movie star is
visiting New York – a comic re-
nowned for obscene stand-up rou-
tines which outrage the gay and
feminist communities, his white
stretch limousine is bound to ap-
pear on Washington Street in the

small hours of the morning and to linger there.

I take up a post beneath a sagging metal awning, half-concealed in the shadows, while Marilyn takes out his compact to check on the goods. He frowns. 'That salt, is terrible for my skin. Suck the moisture right out, sleeping every night on a big pile of salt. Even the rats don't like to live on the salt.' Is that because the rats are worried about their complexions? I wonder. Meantime Marilyn strikes a pose he has borrowed from a Madonna video near the kerb.

Just up the street is Randi, who claims he used to play with the

Harlem Globetrotters. Wearing a leather mini and a red halter, Randi stands six foot eight in heels beneath a sign that says FRANKS SALAMI BOLOGNA LIVERWURST KNOCK-WURST STEW MEATS & SKIRT STEAKS. Truth in advertising.

Down Gansevoort at the edge of the district the neon sign of a fashionable diner emits a pink glow. So very far away – this place where the assholes I went to college with are tossing back parti-coloured drinks and discussing the stock market and interoffice gropings and penetrations. Like my former best friend George Cribbs who wanted to be a poet and works for an ad agency in midtown. We roomed together at

NYU, which I attended for two years and dropped out of because I was way too cool. After George graduated we'd meet for drinks at the Lion's Head or the White Horse Tavern where he thought he was slumming and I felt like an interloper among the gentry. So excited when he first walked in as a freshman with a fake ID from a store on 42nd Street that Dylan Thomas had practically died where we were sitting, but gradually, over the years, he decided that the Welsh bard had wasted and abused his talent. I mean, sure, George admitted, he was great, but what was the matter with being comfortable, taking care of your health, eating sensibly and writing copy for Procter and Gamble in between cranking out those lyrical heart's cries. And I'm on my best behaviour nodding like an idiot coming down off something I smoked or snorted and hoping the bartender won't remember he threw me out three months before. And gradually I think it became too embarrassing for both of us. I stopped calling and Lord knows I don't have a phone, except maybe the open-air unit on the corner of Hudson and 12th. Actually, it's been a relief to quit pretending.

Farther down Washington Street a trio of junkies build a fire in a garbage can, although the night is hot and steamy – the heat of the day, stored up in the concrete and asphalt, coming off now, cooking everyone slowly like so much meat. These old guys, after they been on the street a few years they never really get warm again. The winter cold stays with you in your bones through the long stinking summer and for ever, like a scar. The old farts who wear overcoats and boots in August. Plus that way you don't have to change your clothes for winter. One style fits all. I'm just fine in my black T-shirt and denim jacket which doubles as a blanket, thanks. Be off the street before that happens to me. When I paint my masterpiece. Franks salami bologna.

A red Nissan Z slows to a stop. Marilyn sashays over to the car and schmoozes the driver, turns and waves to me. I come out of the shadow to reveal myself in all my freaky emaciated menace, moon-white face and dyed black hair, my yellow teeth in their bleedy gums. Marilyn zips around to the passenger side and climbs into the Z, which makes the right and slows to a stop half a block down the street where I can still see it. A bum in an overcoat parks his overflowing shopping cart on the sidewalk and peers in the window at the brightly lit diners eating steak frites.

Eventually Marilyn comes back

from his date, adjusting his clothes
and checking his make-up in a
compact, like a model. That's what
he calls it – a date. He hands me a
damp, crumpled fiver. I don't want
to think about the dampness at all. I
want to scrape the bill off my palm
and throw it into the stinking street,
but Marilyn's all excited about being
back at work and planning for the
future. He's talking about how it will
be after the operation, after he gets
married and moves to New Chursey
and I want to slap him and tell him
that it's the land of the living dead.
It's not real, like this fabulous life
we're living here on Gansevoort
Street with its franks salami and
bologna. The flesh they grill on

their Webers out in Morristown comes out of these very malodorous warehouses against which we bravely slouch.

At least Marilyn will be spared the ordeal of having a rotten suburban brat who will grow up to resent and despise him for being a boring submissive suburban housewife.

As the night deepens business picks up and I become nearly ac-customed to the layered stench, the several octaves of decay. The old men sharing a bottle around the fire pass out and the fire dies. I skulk over to Hudson and buy myself a bottle of blackberry brandy to keep my motor running. A dealer strolls by offering coke, crack and smoke.

At first I think no, I'm on duty, but the second time he comes by I have twenty dollars in my pocket from Marilyn and I buy a little rock and fire it up, tickling my brain, making me feel righteous and empowered – I'm here, I'm cool, I'm feeling so good, I'm going to be all right, the future is mine and I'm back on my feet and if I can just smoke a little more of this I'll keep feeling this way instead of slipping back, just a little more to maintain, to stop this fading, to stop this falling away from the perfect moment that was here just a minute ago, to hear that perfect tune in the deep of my brain, that masterpiece.

Franks bologna etcetera.

The buzz has slipped away like a heartbreakingly hot girl at a bar who said she'd be right back in a minute, promise. Leaving me oh so very sad and cranky. Where is the goddamn dealer?

The traffic in and out of the diner picks up around four when the clubs close, yellow cabs pulling up to dispense black-clad party people like Pez, the hip young boys and girls who are not yet ready for bed. I buy a so-called quarter of alleged toot and snort it all at once thinking it will carry me further, slower than smoking rocks.

Marilyn gets eleven dates for the night, a cavalcade of perverts representing several states, classes and ethnic groups, including a Hasid jeweller with the long slinky fore-locks that bounce up and down as he bucks to fulfilment in the front seat of his black Lincoln, a construc-tion worker with Jersey plates in a Subaru still wearing his hardhat and a stretch limo where the guy tells Marilyn he's in the movie business and tips twenty.

The Lambs of God van cruises up, pulls over beside us. The priest says, 'Top of the morning, Marilyn.' He looks surprised, not necessarily happy, when I slink out of my vampire shadow.

'Hello, Father,' says Marilyn. 'You looking for me tonight?'

'No, no, just checking to see that

you're not . . . needing . . . anything.'

'Fine thanks, Father. And you?'

'Bless you and be careful, my
child.' The priest guns the engine
and pulls away.

'Very nice, the Father, but shy,'
says Marilyn, a note of disappoint-
ment in his voice. 'I think maybe
you scare him off.'

'The shy shepherd,' I say.

'I stay at that Lamb of God shelter
one night and he didn't ask me for
nothing,' says Marilyn, as if this
were a heroic feat of selfless minis-
try. 'That day he just cop a little
squeeze when I'm leaving. Food
pretty decent, too.' We watch a
car go by, slowly, the driver look-

ing us over from behind his sunglasses. He seemed about to stop, then he peeled out and tore down the street. After a long pause, Marilyn said, 'My very first date was a priest, when I was an altar boy. He give me some wine.'

'Sounds very romantic,' I say, recalling that I was an altar boy once in another life. I was in awe of my proximity to the sacred rituals. I didn't smoke or swear and I confessed my impure thoughts to the eager priest behind the screen until the day my thoughts transmuted themselves to deeds on Mary Lynch's couch one afternoon, which I failed to mention at my next confession, suffering the guilt of the damned as I slunk away from the confessional booth. When lightning failed to strike me through the days and weeks that followed I began to resent my guilt and then to resent the faith that was so at odds with my secret nature and to exult in my rebellion. And as I turned away from my parents and church I created my own cult to venerate the taboo. Which perverse faith I am stubbornly observing here at five in the morning at the corner of Gansevoort and Washington.

Another car cruises by slowly, a junkyard Buick with two guys in the front seat. The twos are potentially dangerous so I decide I'll show my flag, talk to them myself. I tell

Marilyn to stay put and saunter over to the car. The driver has to open the door because the window doesn't roll down. Two small Hispanic men in their fifties. 'Twenty apiece,' I say, nodding toward Marilyn. 'And you stay on this block.' Finally we agree on thirty-five for two.

I wave Marilyn over and he climbs in the back seat and I'm just leaning back against the building lighting a smoke when Marilyn comes howling and tumbling out of the car, crawling furiously as the car peels out, tyres squealing on the cobblestones. Marilyn flings himself on me and I hold him as he sobs. '*Es mi padre*,' he wails, '*mi padre.*'

'A priest?' I query, hopefully.

He shakes his head violently against my shoulder and suddenly he raises his face and starts apologising for getting make-up on me, wiping at my shoulder, apologising about my jacket, still crying. 'I ruin your jacket,' he says, crying hysterically. It's all I can do to convince him that I don't give a shit about the jacket which started out filthy anyway.

'Are you sure it was . . . him?' I ask.

Gulping air, he nods vehemently. He is sobbing and shaking, and I'm more than a little freaked out myself. I mean, Jesus.

Finally when he has calmed down

35

I suggest we call it a night. 'It's the first time I see him in three years,' Marilyn says. I make him drink the rest of the blackberry brandy and walk him back to the dock in the grainy grey light. As the sun comes up behind us we stand on the edge of the pier and look out over the river at the Maxwell House sign. I can't think of anything to say. I put my arm around him and he sniffles on my shoulder. From a distance we would look like any other couple, I think. Finally I suggest he get some sleep and he picks his way across the rotting boards back to the salt mountain. And that's the end of my career as a pimp.

*   *   *

JAY MCINERNEY

A year after this happened I went back to look for Marilyn. Most of the girls on the street were new to me, but I found Randi, the former Globetrotter, who at first didn't remember me. I do look different now. He thought I was a cop, and then he thought I was a reporter. He wanted money to talk, and finally I gave him ten and he said, 'I remember you, you was that crackhead.' Nice to be remembered. I asked if he had seen Marilyn and he said Marilyn had disappeared suddenly – 'maybe like, I don't know, seems like a year ago'. He couldn't tell me anything and he didn't want to know.

About a year after that I spotted a

wedding announcement in the *Times*. I admit I'd been checking all that time – perusing what we once called the Women's Sports pages – like an idiot, occasionally rewarded with the picture of a high-school or college acquaintance, and then one fine morning I saw a picture that stopped me. Actually, I think I noticed the name first – otherwise I might not have stopped at the picture. Marilyn Bergdorf to wed Ronald Dubowski. It would be just like Marilyn to name himself after a chic department store. I stared at the photo for a long time, and though I wouldn't swear to it in a murder trial I think it was my Marilyn – surgically altered, one presumes – that married Ronald Dubowski, orthodontist, of Oyster Bay, Long Island. I suppose I could have called, but I didn't.

So I don't really know how that night affected Marilyn, if it changed his life, if he is officially and anatomically a woman, now, or even if he is alive. I do know that lives can change overnight, though it usually takes much longer than that to comprehend that it has happened, to sense that we have changed direction. A week after Marilyn almost had sex with his father I checked myself into Phoenix House. I called my parents for the first time in more than a year. Now, two years later, I have a

boring job and a crummy apart-
ment and a girlfriend who makes
the rest of it seem almost OK. I'd
be lying if I said there aren't times I
miss the old days, or that I don't
breathe a huge sigh of relief when I
climb on the train after a few hours
spent visiting my parents, or that it's
a gas being straight all the time, but
still I'm grateful to be where I am
now.

You think you're living a secret
and temporary life, underground, in
the dark. You don't imagine that
someone will drive up the street, or
walk in the door or look through
the window – someone who will
reveal you to yourself not as you
hope to be in some glorious future

metamorphosis but as you find
yourself at that moment. Whatever
you are doing then, you will have to
stop and say, 'Yes, this is me.'

A NOTE ON THE AUTHOR

Jay McInerney has written five novels including *Bright Lights, Big City* and *Brightness Falls*. His most recent novel is *The Last of the Savages*. He lives in New York and Tennessee.

Margaret Atwood	*The Labrador Fiasco*
T. Coraghessan Boyle	*She Wasn't Soft*
Nadine Gordimer	*Harald, Claudia, and their Son Duncan*
David Guterson	*The Drowned Son*
Candia McWilliam	*Change of Use*
Will Self	*A Story for Europe*
Patrick Süskind	*Maître Mussard's Bequest*
Joanna Trollope	*Faith*
Tobias Wolff	*Two Boys and a Girl*

Selected poetry of Matthew Arnold
Selected poetry of William Blake
Selected poetry of Rupert Brooke
Selected poetry of Elizabeth Barrett Browning
Selected poetry of Robert Browning
Selected poetry of Robert Burns
Selected poetry of Lord Byron
Selected poetry of John Clare
Selected poetry of Samuel Taylor Coleridge
Selected poetry of Emily Dickinson
Selected poetry of John Donne
Selected poetry of John Dryden
Selected poetry of Thomas Hardy
Selected poetry of Robert Herrick
Selected poetry of Gerard Manley Hopkins
Selected poetry of John Keats
Selected poetry of Rudyard Kipling
Selected poetry of D. H. Lawrence
Selected poetry of Andrew Marvell
Selected poetry of John Milton
Selected poetry of Wilfred Owen
Selected poetry of Alexander Pope
Selected poetry of Christina Rossetti
Selected poetry of Walter Scott
Selected poetry of William Shakespeare
Selected poetry of P. B. Shelley
Selected poetry of Alfred Lord Tennyson
Selected poetry of Edward Thomas
Selected poetry of Walt Whitman
Selected poetry of Oscar Wilde
Selected poetry of William Wordsworth
Selected poetry of W. B. Yeats